English BASICS

FOR AGES 10-11 KEY STAGE 2

KU-494-957

Contents

Look and learn

button

celebrate

> Sometimes vowels in longer words are **not stressed**, or pronounced. These vowels are often difficult to hear. The words above both contain **unstressed vowels**.

Practice

Fill in the missing unstressed vowels in each word below. Use a dictionary if necessary.

1. env_e_lope

2. b_u_s_y_ness

3. comp_a_ny

4. entr_a_nce

5. ment_a_l

6. photogr_a_pher

7. diction_a_ry

8. valu_a_ble

9. secr_e_t_a_ry

10. int_e_rest

11. cem_e_t_e_ry

12. trav_e_l

Challenge

Join up the syllables.

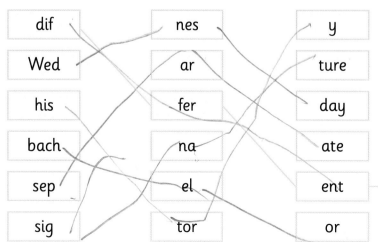

dif	nes	y
Wed	ar	ture
his	fer	day
bach	na	ate
sep	el	ent
sig	tor	or

Write the word and underline any unstressed vowels.

1. IVO _____

2. NO _____

3. NO _____

4. NO _____

5. ~~different~~ IVO _____

6. IVO _____

Look and learn

A **root word** is a word to which **prefixes** or **suffixes** may be added.
Sometimes the root word is **easy** to see. Sometimes the root word is **harder** to work out.

unhelpful (root word – help)

flexibility (root word – flexible)

Practice

Find and write the root word of each longer word below.

1. bicycle   cycle
2. triangle   _No_
3. exported   _No_
4. injustice   _No_
5. friendliness   _No_
6. uncontrollable   _No_
7. admission   _No_
8. magically   _No_
9. disagreement   _No_
10. signature   _No_
11. competition   _No_
12. proposal   _No_
13. generously   _No_
14. unsuitable   _No_
15. sympathise   _No_

Challenge

Add prefixes and suffixes. Make at least two longer words from each root word.

root word	longer words
appear	disappear, appearing
cover	_No_
like	_No_
comfort	_No_
colour	_No_
weak	_No_

Look and learn

A **dash** holds words apart. It is stronger than a comma. It is not as strong as a full stop.

Brackets enclose information to show it is separate from the rest of the sentence.

Sam ordered his favourite meal – curry.

The Pyramids (found in Egypt) are huge.

Practice

Choose the best ending to complete each sentence.

Sentence endings
a marvellous invention.
or you'll be in trouble.
she had pink hair.
all green and slimy.
football!
my old teddy.
Treasure Island.
I hate it!
for painting a picture.
a silver one.

1. There is only one sport worth playing – _____football!_____

2. My sister loves pop music – _____

3. John Logie Baird invented television – _____

4. I have got a mountain bike – _____

5. One girl was different – _____

6. I read a great book last week – _____

7. Get your homework in on time – _____

8. Tom won a competition – _____

9. The monster appeared – _____

10. In the attic I found an old friend – _____

Challenge

Choose the best "filling" to go inside each pair of brackets.

| over 26 miles | a red sports car | in Africa | a famous composer | 1666 |

1. The Great Fire of London (_____) was terrible.

2. Mount Kilimanjaro (_____) always has snow at the top.

3. Beethoven (_____) wrote lots of music.

4. Each year there is a marathon (_____) in New York.

5. The man parked his car (_____).

Look and learn

Words may be divided into groups called **parts of speech**. Three important parts of speech are: **nouns**, **verbs** and **adjectives**.

This is a **noun**. It is a **naming word**.

The happy lady was laughing.

This is an **adjective**. It is a **describing word**. It tells us more about the **noun**.

This is a **verb**. It is a word that describes **actions**.

Practice

In the following sentences:
circle the adjectives; tick the nouns; underline the verbs.

1. I <u>tripped</u> over the uneven floor. ✓

2. The silly boy crashed his new bike.

3. When the old lady reached her house, she sat down.

4. We saw wild horses in the forest.

5. The large crowd cheered as the skilful player scored.

6. The giggling girls annoyed the teacher.

7. A prickly hedgehog snuffled in the dry leaves.

8. The lazy man was sleeping under the tall tree.

Challenge

Think of a suitable word for each gap. In the brackets write if it is a noun, verb or adjective.

1. Sam put the ___NO___ suitcase on the floor. (___NO___)

2. Athens is the capital of ___NO___ . (___NO___)

3. The mountaineers ___NO___ to the summit. (___NO___)

4. The children sang loudly at the ___NO___ . (___NO___)

5. The cat's ___NO___ was soft and silky. (___NO___)

6. The helicopter ___NO___ over the motorway. (___NO___)

5

Look and learn

The thief **stole** the jewels.

The jewels **were stolen** by the thief.

> A verb is **active** when the subject of the sentence does the action.

> A verb is **passive** when the subject of the sentence has the action done to it.

Practice

Underline the verb in the each sentence. Say if it is active (A) or passive (P).

1. The lion <u>chased</u> the deer. (A)
2. The car was driven by the lady. (___)
3. The author wrote lots of books. (___)
4. The doctor listened to my heart. (___)
5. The cup was won by the girls. (___)
6. The tree was chopped down by the man. (___)
7. The river ran through the valley. (___)
8. The candle was blown out by the wind. (___)
9. The child bought some sweets. (___)
10. The avalanche crashed down the mountain. (___)
11. The goal was scored by Jess. (___)
12. The dog chased the cat. (___)

Challenge

Rewrite each sentence. Change the verb from passive to active.

1. The car was stopped by the police officer.   The police officer stopped the car.
2. My luggage was carried by a porter.   _____
3. The mouse was chased by the cat.   _____
4. The gold medal was won by the relay team.   _____
5. The coin was picked up by the boy.   _____
6. The window was broken by the girl.   _____
7. The glass was dropped by Sam.   _____
8. The carrot was eaten by the horse.   _____
9. All the keys were stolen by the thief.   _____
10. Ben was hugged by his aunt.   _____

Look and learn

English is not just **one language**. It is made up of words taken from many **other languages**.

spaghetti

Italy

jungle

India

ballet

France

yacht

Holland

Practice

Fill in each gap with a word from the Word Box.

Here are some words that come from France.

Word Box

duvet	banquet
ballet	buffet
bracket	cabaret
trumpet	sachet
scarlet	ricochet
bouquet	blanket

1. ____Scarlet____ is a dark red colour.
2. A _____ holds up a shelf.
3. A _____ is a bunch of flowers.
4. A _____ is a small packet.
5. A _____ is a musical instrument.
6. A _____ is a bed covering, filled with feathers.
7. A _____ is a number of different acts.
8. _____ is a kind of dance.
9. A _____ is a special feast.
10. A _____ is a bed covering.
11. A _____ is a meal where you serve yourself.
12. A _____ is when something hits a surface and bounces off.

Challenge

Use a dictionary to help you. Decide which country each word comes from.

Word	Country of origin
1. pizza	
2. schooner	
3. café	
4. kangaroo	
5. wok	
6. moccasins	
7. bungalow	
8. reggae	

There is a word from each of these countries: France, America, Jamaica, China, Italy, India, Australia, Holland.

9

Look and learn

The English language has been influenced by **many other languages**. Understanding the **origins** of words sometimes helps us spell them.

In Latin 'signum' means 'a sign'.

From the word 'signum' we get the words 'signal' and 'signature'.

Practice

Complete the chart correctly with words from the Word Box.

	Latin word	Meaning	English words
1.	signum	a sign	signal, signature
2.	scribere	to write	
3.	videre	to see	
4.	pedum	foot	
5.	gratus	pleasing	
6.	specare	to look	
7.	liber	free	
8.	civis	citizen	

Word Box	
describe	pedal
congratulate	vision
spectator	signal
evident	liberty
liberal	grateful
signature	city
civilian	pedestrian
spectacles	scribble

Challenge

Complete the chart with some words you think might come from these Greek words:

	Greek word	Meaning	English words
1.	phone	sound	telephone, microphone
2.	geo	earth	
3.	auto	self	
4.	graph	to write	
5.	aster	a star	
6.	scope	I see	

Look and learn

Alice found a key   which opened the door.

| main clause | subordinate clause |

Many complex sentences are made up of a **main clause**
and a **subordinate clause** (a less important clause).

Practice

Join up each main clause from Set A with an appropriate subordinate clause from Set B.

Set A

1. The children began to shout
2. Last night I read a good book
3. Alexander Bell was the inventor
4. I visited Athens
5. I collect stamps
6. Samuel Pepys lived in London

Set B

when I went to bed.
which is in Greece.
because they are so colourful.
when the teacher left the room.
when the Great Fire spread in 1666.
who invented the telephone.

Write the sentences you have made:

1. _____
2. _____
3. _____
4. _____
5. _____
6. _____

Challenge

Think of a suitable subordinate clause to finish each complex sentence:

1. I like cats because _____ .

2. My pet rabbit escaped when _____ .

3. I climbed the tree so that _____ .

4. I saw the queen when _____ .

5. The explorer kept walking until _____ .

6. The snake slithered through the grass just as _____ .

Look and learn

> **lubricate**
> to oil or grease the moving parts of a machine so they run smoothly.

You can use a dictionary to find the **meaning** of a word and to check its **spelling**.

Practice

Use a dictionary to help you solve these clues. They are in alphabetical order.

1. A _crobat_ Someone who does balancing tricks.　**2.** B_____ Lovely – very pretty.

3. C_____ Stops wine coming out of a bottle.　**4.** D_____ Not safe – risky.

5. E_____ Costs a lot.　**6.** F_____ A shallow river crossing.

7. G_____ A quick look.　**8.** H_____ A six-sided shape.

9. I_____ A pointed stick of ice.　**10.** J_____ Make fun of person in rude way.

11. K_____ A sharp cutting tool.　**12.** L_____ A long spear carried by knights.

13. M_____ Something worn over the face.　**14.** N_____ Not wide.

15. O_____ A sea creature with tentacles.　**16.** P_____ Quiet and calm.

17. Q_____ Where ships moor.　**18.** R_____ Not long ago.

19. S_____ Rare.　**20.** T_____ A shop assistant puts money in it.

21. U_____ To join together.　**22.** V_____ Not clear.

23. W_____ Clever and amusing.　**24.** X_____ A short form of Christmas.

25. Y_____ A type of sailing boat　**26.** Z_____ To move or climb suddenly.

Challenge

Spell these words correctly. Use a dictionary to help.

1. calender _____calendar_____　**2.** resevoir _____

3. parliment _____　**4.** goverment _____

5. delicous _____　**6.** dissappear _____

7. somersalt _____

8. alltogether _____

9. sissors _____

10. kangeroo _____

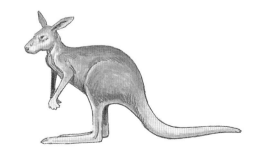

16

Spelling rules

Look and learn

Some **spelling rules** are helpful to remember. One of the more commonly quoted rules is:

i (when it makes the sound **ee**) before **e** except after **c**

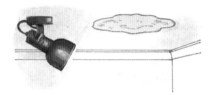

I bel**ie**ve the th**ie**f stole a p**ie**ce of cake.

The pancake is on the c**ei**ling!

Practice

Make these words.

ie

1. ach___ve   **2.** bel___ve   **3.** br___f   **4.** ch___f   **5.** f___ld

achieve   _____   _____   _____   _____

ie

6. sh___ld   **7.** p___ce   **8.** s___ge   **9.** bab___s   **10.** cop___s

_____   _____   _____   _____   _____

ei

11. c___ling   **12.** rec___ve   **13.** dec___ve   **14.** perc___ve   **15.** conc___t

_____   _____   _____   _____   _____

Challenge

Follow the rule! Choose **ie** or **ei**. Check in a dictionary if you are not sure.

1. pr___st   **2.** misch___f

3. dec___t   **4.** rel___f

5. c___ling   **6.** n___ce

7. shr___k   **8.** s___ve

9. conc___ted   **10.** y___ld

11. rec___ve   **12.** f___rce

NB: There are some words which don't stick to the rules!

seize

weird

forfeit

17

Look and learn

Why runnest thou hither and thither?

The **astronauts** prepared for **countdown**.

Many **words** and **expressions** have **changed**.

New words enter our language all the time.

Practice

Match up the old and new version of the words and phrases.

1.	wilt	lives
2.	saith	truly
3.	abides	will
4.	ye	look at
5.	verily	says
6.	wondrous	are
7.	behold	wonderful
8.	art	you

9.	over yonder	Do as you are told.
10.	hither and thither	What do you want?
11.	Do as thou art bidden.	Who lives here?
12.	to tarry awhile	over there
13.	What dost thou desire?	Are you a friend or an enemy?
14.	Art thou friend or foe?	Come here.
15.	Who abides within?	to stay for a while
16.	Come nigh.	here and there

Challenge

Tick which of these words you think have entered our language in the last 50 years.

mobile phone	pen	television
farm	computer	satellite
wheelie	house	video
calculator	dinosaur	cheeseburger
mill	sneaker	trainers
floppy disk	chimney	motel
wood	Internet	astronaut

Look and learn

Keep quiet!

We speak to each other **informally**.

You are forbidden to engage in conversation.

OFFICIAL NOTICE

Official language is very **formal**.

Practice

Match up these formal and informal ways of saying things.

1. Can you decipher my writing?   Thanks for the gift.

2. Kindly append your signature.   Please answer my letter.

3. Many thanks for your donation.   Keep off the grass.

4. I regret I am unable to attend.   Get out of my way.

5. Please reply to my correspondence.   Can you read my writing?

6. I bid you farewell.   Pay up at once.

7. Please desist from walking on the grass.   Sorry I can't come.

8. Apologies for any inconvenience caused.   Cheerio.

9. Do not hinder my progress.   Sorry to have bothered you.

10. Kindly settle your debt immediately.   Please sign this.

Challenge

Write what you think these formal notices mean.

1. Thieves will be prosecuted.

2. Vehicular travel prohibited.

3. You are requested not to consume your food on these premises.

4. Concealing information is a punishable offence.

5. Kindly register on entry.

6. The management cannot accept any liability for theft.

Look and learn

We can often change a **root word** by adding a **prefix**.

zzkflmpjx!

My name is Luke.

We can often change a **root word** by adding a **suffix**.

nonsense   sense   sensible
(root word + prefix)   (root word)   (root word + suffix)

Practice

Choose a prefix from the box to complete each word.

mis	out	dis	extra
for	hemi	mid	trans
post	retro	under	
be	sub	with	sur

1. __mid__ air   **2.** _____ stand

3. _____ cast   **4.** _____ current

5. _____ friend   **6.** _____ behave

7. _____ code   **8.** _____ face

9. _____ grade   **10.** _____ approve

11. _____ bid   **12.** _____ sphere

13. _____ plant   **14.** _____ ordinary

15. _____ marine

Challenge

Take the suffix off each word. Write the root word correctly.

1. historian   __history__   **2.** beggar _____

3. observatory _____   **4.** reception _____

5. president _____   **6.** kingdom _____

7. argument _____   **8.** cowardice _____

9. magnetism _____   **10.** friendship _____

11. apologise _____   **12.** sparkle _____

13. simplify _____   **14.** cyclist _____

Look and learn

The chips were cold | when I ate them.

main clause | subordinate clause

A **complex** sentence contains a **main clause** and a **subordinate** (less important) **clause**. The subordinate clause may not make sense on its own.

Practice

Circle the main clause and underline the subordinate clause in each sentence.

1. The wind was so cold that I put on a coat.

2. The dog dug a hole for his bone so he could bury it.

3. When I am eighteen, I am allowed to vote.

4. Until I look, I don't know what the time is.

5. Tidy up your bedroom before you get into trouble.

6. Unless you look in the cupboard, you will never find your present.

7. While the fire engines were on the way, the house burnt down.

8. Whenever I can, I go to watch Manchester United play football.

9. It often rains in November so I carry an umbrella.

10. You cannot have any sweets until you wash up.

Please note – the main clause does not always come at the beginning!

Challenge

Complete these complex sentences by adding a subordinate clause of your own.

1. P.C. Jolly arrested the man who _____.

2. Anna bought a magazine which _____.

3. I found the treasure which _____.

4. Mr Desai was a teacher who _____.

5. Tom did not get up even though _____.

6. We saw many new clothes shops when _____.

7. Mrs Smith thanked me for _____.

8. The dog went to sleep after _____.

Look and learn

Shireen slipped over   in a muddy puddle.

clause   phrase

A **clause** may be used either as a **whole sentence** or as a **part of a sentence**. A clause always contains a **verb**.

A **phrase** does **not** contain a **verb**.
A phrase does **not make sense** on its own.

Practice

Choose a phrase from the phrase box to complete each sentence.

1. The baby chicks followed <u>behind the hen</u> _____.
2. The lion pounced, _____.
3. The man carried a bag, _____.
4. _____, it rained hard.
5. Tom did his spellings _____.
6. The alien spacecraft landed _____.
7. _____ I felt a lot better.
8. The children looked up at the _____ clouds.
9. _____ we go on holiday.
10. _____ I managed to lift the heavy rock.

Phrase Box

full of dirty washing
carelessly and untidily
After my medicine
Every summer
behind the hen
With great effort
dark, rainy
quick as a flash
During the night
on the playground

Challenge

Write if each of these is a phrase (P) or a clause (C).

1. The balloons popped. (C)   2. after the party (__)

3. long and loud (__)   4. They moved quietly. (__)

5. with a sigh (__)   6. as flat as a pancake (__)

7. We skipped. (__)   8. It rained heavily. (__)

9. thunder and lightning (__)   10. before breakfast (__)

11. in a while (__)   12. The wind roared. (__)

More punctuation

Look and learn

It is important to check that your punctuation is correct!

The pilot landed in his car. He drove home.

The pilot landed. In his car, he drove home.

Practice

Tick (✓) the sentences that are correctly punctuated. Cross (✗) those that are wrong.

1. After a while the car, an old wreck, rattled by. ☐
2. The boy shouted, "Please help!" ☐
3. I'm glad you came; it's been a long time. ☐
4. Leroys' pencil was broken ☐
5. Mrs Jones asked where is my bag? ☐
6. At the bottom of the sign it said: "No entry". ☐
7. The Great Plague (1665) was followed by the Great Fire (1666). ☐
8. The monster shook it's head. ☐
9. "They're not ripe yet, the gardener explained. ☐
10. The winning numbers were: 7, 42, 47 and 50. ☐
11. The boy's bikes had been stolen when they returned. ☐
12. The plane its engine in flames began to head towards the mountain. ☐

Challenge

Rewrite this passage. Punctuate it correctly.

marc and shireen decided to climb mount kilimanjaro after a while they stopped what a marvellous view exclaimed shireen as they progressed further marcs foot slipped he almost fell its too dangerous for me he said Im going down again

_____

_____

_____

_____

Look and learn

There is a rum**our** that a creat**ure** lives in the lake.

It is helpful to learn the spelling of common word endings.

Practice

Choose either **our** or **ure** to complete each word.

1. nat _ure_
2. flav____
3. fail____
4. hum____

5. rum____
6. temperat____
7. neighb____
8. fig____

9. harb____
10. treas____
11. fut____
12. vig____

13. inj____
14. glam____
15. splend____
16. pleas____

17. vap____
18. advent____
19. mixt____
20. hon____

Use a dictionary if you are not sure!

Challenge

Use some of the words you made to complete these definitions.

1. _____Rumour_____ Something passed around as news – but may not be true.

2. _____ Strength. Energy.

3. _____ To harm oneself.

4. _____ The inability to do something.

5. _____ The taste of something.

6. _____ The time ahead.

7. _____ Steam or mist.

8. _____ Someone who lives nearby.

9. _____ A sense of fun.

10. _____ Something that has been mixed.

11. _____ Something that pleases.

12. _____ A place where ships dock.

Look and learn

machin**ery**

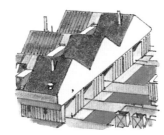

fact**ory**

libr**ary**

It is helpful to learn the spelling of common word endings.

Practice

Choose either **ery**, **ory** or **ary** to complete each word.

1. nurs_ery_

2. laborat____

3. gran____

4. fact____

5. diction____

6. discov____

7. conservat____

8. milit____

9. brew____

10. dormit____

11. libr____

12. estu____

13. refect____

14. bak____

15. scen____

16. deliv____

17. direct____

18. di____

19. mock____

20. jewell____

Use a dictionary if you are not sure!

Challenge

Sort the words you made into sets. Add two more words to each set.

ery words	**ory** words	**ary** words

29

Similes

Look and learn

A **simile** is when one thing is compared to another using the words **as** or **like**.

My tyre was **as** flat **as** a pancake.

When my mum cleans up she's **like** a whirlwind.

Practice

Match up the beginnings and endings of these common similes.

1. as tough as — mouse

2. as blind as a — cucumber

3. as quiet as a — grass

4. as busy as a — leather

5. as green as — elephant

6. as smooth as — feather

7. as cool as a — bat

8. as brave as a — silk

9. as light as a — lion

10. as heavy as an — bee

Challenge

Make up some similes of your own to finish these sentences.

1. On a stormy day the wind is like _____.

2. When Tom is happy he is like _____.

3. When Sita gets angry she is like _____.

4. The hot sun was like _____.

5. The motorbike roared past like _____.

6. When I went on the Big Dipper it felt like _____.

7. The candyfloss tasted like _____.

8. The monster hissed like _____.

Look and learn

We can learn a lot by playing **word games**.
They can help us with spelling and help
improve our vocabulary.

Practice

Use a dictionary to help you solve this puzzle.

1. a bubbly drink

c	h	a	m	p	a	g	n	e

2. a very prickly desert plant

c	a		

3. to hold fast to

c	l			

4. one hundred years

c	e			

5. to get in touch with

c	o					

6. a spice used to flavour food

c	i					

7. a young swan

c	y		

8. to bend low

c	r			

9. a smooth bend

c	u			

10. a hot, spicy meal

c	u			

Challenge

Match up the pairs of letters in the box with the letters below to form the names of creatures.

1. heron   **2.** _____mmoth   **3.** _____nx

4. _____libut   **5.** _____zzard   **6.** _____oat

7. _____ail   **8.** _____lchard   **9.** _____strel

10. _____lmon   **11.** _____eetah   **12.** _____out

he	st	qu	ke	sa	ly
tr	ch	pi	bu	ha	ma

Answers

Page 2
Practice: 1. envelope, 2. business, 3. company, 4. entrance, 5. mental, 6. photographer, 7. dictionary, 8. valuable, 9. secretary, 10. interest, 11. cemetery, 12. travel
Challenge: 1. hist_o_ry, 2. sign_a_ture, 3. Wedn_e_sday, 4. sep_a_rate, 6. bach_e_lor

Page 3
Practice: 2. angle, 3. port, 4. just, 5. friend, 6. control, 7. admit, 8. magic, 9. agree, 10. sign, 11. compete, 12. propose, 13. generous, 14. suit, 15. sympathy
Challenge: answers may vary

Page 4
Practice: 1. football! 2. I hate it!
3. a marvellous invention. 4. a silver one.
5. she had pink hair. 6. Treasure Island.
7. or you'll be in trouble.
8. for painting a picture.
9. all green and slimy. 10. my old teddy.
Challenge: 1. 1666, 2. in Africa,
3. a famous composer, 4. over 26 miles,
5. a red sports car

Page 5
Practice:
1. tripped (verb), uneven (adjective), floor (noun)
2. silly, new (adjectives), boy, bike (nouns), crashed (verb)
3. old (adjective), lady, house (nouns), reached, sat (verb)
4. saw (verb), wild (adjective), horses, forest (nouns)
5. large, skilful (adjectives), cheered, scored (verbs), crowd, player (nouns)
6. giggling (adjective), girls, teacher (nouns), annoyed (verb)
7. prickly, dry (adjectives), hedgehog, leaves (nouns), snuffled (verb)
8. lazy, tall (adjectives), man, tree (nouns), was sleeping (verb)
Challenge: answers may vary

Page 6
Practice: 1. so that, 2. when, 3. who, 4. whenever, 5. in case, 6. so that, 7. as, 8. before, 9. because, 10. when
Challenge: answers may vary

Page 7
Practice: 1. bi, 2. sub, 3. aero, 4. im 5. in, 6. ir, 7. tri, 8. il, 9. pre, 10. de, 11. mis, 12. re, 13. centi, 14. anti, 15. ex
Challenge: 1. baby, 2. nasty, 3. beauty, 4. quarrel, 5. shine, 6. operate, 7. knife, 8. microscope, 9. burgle, 10. mystery, 11. attend, 12. excite

Page 8
Practice: 2. was driven (P), 3. wrote (A), 4. listened (A), 5. was won (P), 6. was chopped (P), 7. ran (A), 8. was blown (P), 9. bought (A), 10. crashed (A), 11. was scored (P), 12. chased (A)
Challenge:
2. A porter carried my luggage.
3. The cat chased the mouse.
4. The relay team won the gold medal.
5. The boy picked up the coin.
6. The girl broke the window.
7. Sam dropped the glass.
8. The horse ate the carrot.
9. The thief stole all the keys.
10. Ben's aunt hugged him.

Page 9
Practice: 1. Scarlet, 2. bracket, 3. bouquet, 4. sachet, 5. trumpet, 6. duvet, 7. cabaret, 8. ballet, 9. banquet, 10. blanket, 11. buffet, 12. ricochet
Challenge: 1. Italy, 2. Holland, 3. France, 4. Australia, 5. China, 6. America, 7. India, 8. Jamaica

Page 10
Practice: 2. separate, 3. favourite, 4. bicycle, 5. conscience, 6. piece, 7. young, 8. believe, 9. miserable, 10. weight
Challenge: answers may vary

Page 11
Practice:
1. The man asked, "Is it raining?"
2. "I've lost my pen," Rohan shouted.
3. The burglar whispered, "Someone's coming!"
4. "Where's my bag?" Mrs Shah asked.
5. You will need a pen, a ruler and some paper.
6. The noise, a loud banging noise, was awful.
7. The children's clothes were on the floor.
8. "What a lovely surprise!" the teacher said.
9. "Pass the salt, please," Sam's dad asked.
10. The boy's coat was torn.
Challenge: Danger? No. Swimming allowed!

Page 12
Practice: 2. scribble, describe, 3. vision, evident, 4. pedal, pedestrian, 5. grateful, congratulate, 6. spectator, spectacles, 7. liberty, liberal, 8. city, civilian
Challenge: answers may vary

Page 13
Practice:
1. The children began to shout when the teacher left the room.
2. Last night I read a good book when I went to bed.
3. Alexander Bell was the inventor who invented the telephone.
4. I visited Athens which is in Greece.
5. I collect stamps because they are so colourful.
6. Samuel Pepys lived in London during the Great Fire in 1666.
Challenge: answers may vary

Page 14
Practice: 1. cooks, 2. speed, 3. served, 4. never, 5. well, 6. clean, 7. nine, 8. one, 9. worm, 10. birds
Challenge:
1. has a silver lining.
2. make most noise.
3. in one basket.
4. run deep.
5. deserves another.
6. gathers no moss.
7. think alike but fools seldom differ.
8. into the fire.

Page 15
Practice: 2. umbrella, 3. confident, 4. electric, 5. infected, 6. introduce, 7. chatterbox, 8. hospital, 9. restlessness, 10. remember, 11. different, 12. January, 13. attention, 14. uniform, 15. conductor
Challenge: 2. Nov_e_mber, 3. prop_o_sal, 4. helpl_e_ssly, helpf_u_lly, 5. adv_e_nture, 6. lem_o_nade, 7.exc_e_llent, 8. dis_a_ster, 9. conf_i_dent, 10. exp_e_nsive, ext_e_nsive

Page 16
Practice: 2. Beautiful, 3. Cork, 4. Dangerous, 5. Expensive, 6. Ford, 7. Glance, 8. Hexagon, 9. Icicle, 10. Jeer, 11. Knife, 12. Lance, 13. Mask, 14. Narrow, 15. Octopus , 16. Peaceful, 17. Quay, 18. Recent, 19. Scarce, 20. Till, 21. Unite, 22. Vague, 23. Witty, 24. Xmas, 25. Yacht, 26. Zoom
Challenge: 2. reservoir, 3. parliament, 4. government, 5. delicious, 6. disappear, 7. somersault, 8. altogether,9. scissors, 10. kangaroo

Page 17
Practice: 2. believe, 3. brief, 4. chief, 5. field, 6. shield, 7. piece, 8. siege, 9. babies, 10. copies, 11. ceiling, 12. receive, 13. deceive, 14. perceive, 15. conceit
Challenge: 1. priest, 2. mischief, 3. deceit, 4. relief, 5. ceiling, 6. niece, 7. shriek, 8. sieve, 9. conceited, 10. yield, 11. receive, 12. fierce